WINTER LEGENDS AND LORE

WINTER LEGENDS AND LORE

By: Chad Lewis

ISBN: 978-1-7338026-5-9

Printed in the United States by Documation

www.chadlewisresearch.com

Cover Design: Rick Fisk
Lumberjacks and Babe the Blue Ox Illustrations by Rick Fisk
All other Illustrations by: Morgan Knudsen

Dedication

This book is dedicated to Leo Lewis, whose never-ending love of all things winter and Christmas is extremely contagious.

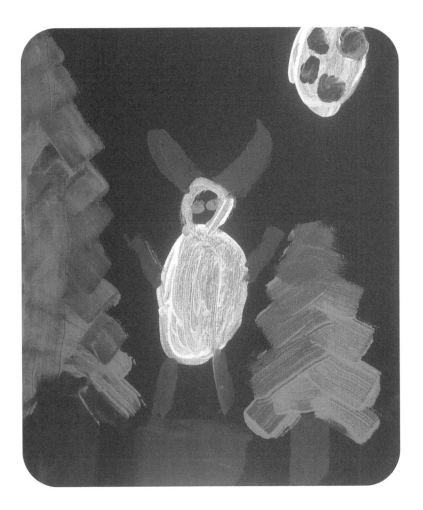

Acknowledgments

First and foremost, I have to give a huge thank you to my friend and colleague Morgan Knudsen, who not only did the wonderful foreword, she is responsible for the amazing artwork in this guide. She will certainly be on Santa's nice list!

I have a ton of respect to all those people who have lived in some of the harshest weather possible and survived winter to pass on these legends and customs

I owe a humongous debt of gratitude to my mother Judy Lewis whose love of all things Christmas has certainly been passed to all of us in the family.

The wonderful cover art was done by the talented Rick Fisk.

A big thank you to Jerry Hajewski for once again making my research better.

A warm cup of hot tallow goes out to my fellow Wendigo adventurers Kevin Lee Nelson and Noah Voss who have helped me survive numerous Wendigo expeditions.

As always, I have to thank the most important winter creatures in my life—Nisa Giaquinto and Leo Lewis.

Introduction

Many people wrongly believe that Halloween is the spookiest time of the year. However, the goal of this book is to correct this erroneous belief. I feel that after reading all of these fantastic tales of ghosts, witches, and werewolves, you will discover that Halloween cannot hold a jack-o-lantern candle to the creepiness that occurs during the darkest days of the year.

Why is winter such a terrifying time of the year? Imagine living in a cold climate over 150 years ago. A time when you may have lived in a small one-room cabin with no running water, no indoor plumbing, no furnace or electricity, all while constantly worrying that your stored provisions might not be enough to stave off starvation. This was a time when the overwhelming majority of people lived and worked on the family farm. When winter came, all the plants, crops, and bushes withered and died, and there was no guarantee that they would return the following season. During these times, winter was literally a live and death scenario for the majority of people.

On a more supernatural level, winter was also the time of year when evil spirits and supernatural beings had free reign to roam the earth, as more darkness meant more secretive hours to torment humans. These sinister beings were thought to be lurking in every nook and cranny, just biding their time until you let your guard down long enough for them to attack. This was a time when many believed that hordes of werewolves were prowling the woods in search of humans to devour. Witches flew under the cover of darkness to recruit new members and attack and kill the innocent. The *Cincinnati Commercial* newspaper put the fear of the winter season succinctly when they wrote on January 20, 1873, that winter is when "All infernal, limboed, or otherwise uncanny spirits are abroad in unwonted power."

It is comforting to realize that throughout history no one has had an easier time surviving the harshness of the season than we do today. Most of us enjoy many luxuries that we take for granted, luxuries that were completely unimaginable in the old days—things like indoor plumbing, electricity, heat, endless in-home entertainment possibilities, and enough food to survive the season, Yet, here in America, every year millions of people suffer from Seasonal Affective Disorder (SAD). Experts contend that a lack of vitamin D, a lack of sunlight, poor eating habits, and nearly non-existent exercise all combine to produce a sense of melancholy or depression that hits us hard during the winter months. The good news is that doctors believe that by simply reversing all of the above-mentioned causes of SAD, we can generally improve our overall mood and outlook on life during these dark times. For me, when the sadness of the season sets in—as I grumble that there is nothing interesting to watch on Netflix, it helps me to think back to my ancestors living in their unforgiving dark reality—when I do that, the winter season seems exponentially more doable.

So, what do I hope you take from this book? I hope that when you finish reading all of these terrific customs, rituals, and folklore, that the season will take on a greater significance and importance in your life. I personally take great comfort and solace in knowing that people from all across the world have been performing these customs for thousands of years. In today's world, you will undoubtedly hear someone griping about the fact that the holiday season has become too commercialized. No longer is the season about spending quality time with your loved ones, giving back to the community, or even exchanging heartfelt gifts with one another in celebration of the season. Instead, it has been infected with greed, commercialism, and a sadistic competition to see who can spend the most money on stuff we truly do not desire or need. And while I tend to generally agree with this sentiment, I ask—who says it has to be this way? Once you know the true reason we decorate our trees, why we go caroling, or why we open our doors and windows on New Year's Eve, it transforms the season into the most festive, most meaningful, and perhaps even the most fulfilling time of the year. That is what I hope you get from this book.

Foreword

Monsters don't live in the dark. Monsters live in the cold. The darkness simply follows.

Darkness is a symptom of the environment while the cold is a state of being which exists on a particle level. We cannot *be* dark. When we walk into a room there is no dark switch, but we can be cold, and the cold and the dark operate in sync. They are inseparable, whether you live in a vast desert or a wooded winter forest. They are an unspeakable and deadly marriage: the darkness hides our sins while the cold keeps them silent.

I live in the northern most populated city of Canada, Edmonton, Alberta, and as I write this, it is -45C. Our temperatures can reach the levels of Siberia and we have been known to be one of the coldest places on the planet throughout the winter months. I have been a student of parapsychology for two decades. My family influence in the paranormal goes back a century, yet it's hard to find someone else that will fall in love with monsters like I did. I knew when I met Chad and we connected over our mutual fascination of the Wendigo, the First Nations water spirit invoked by hunger, trauma and famine, that I had met my match. Although we are miles apart, standing on the steps of Swift Runner's gallows (the first man to be legally hung in relation to such a possession), hearing the howl of the Wendigo on the shores of the frozen lakes, and stepping into the giant footsteps of the greatest winter legend had an effect the Wendigo did *not* intend: although it is a monster of isolation, its influence, for us, became one of great connection.

Folklore is the realism of the mind and it is a connecting thread binding our humanity to our cultures: it is a glimpse into the human consciousness that *creates* our culture. Legends of monsters and whimsy don't always come from people simply "making up stories"; they often allude to far greater truths if one is willing to listen in the right way. Folklore may be true or false, but it is always a glimpse into something humanity got right and often, they are stories based on experiences, not experiences based on stories. The monsters of winter legend are echoes of something greater than children's bedtime stories, and they often are used to describe a reality we are simply not daring enough to face. The monsters and mystical creatures are a part of us and many times, they are realized thoughts that we turn into fairy tales in order to make them manageable. Sometimes, they are the consciousness within our consciousness and, sometimes, they gain enough momentum to leave footprints in the snow in what we call reality. That's what makes winter folklore so frightening: it is real, both as part of us and as an extension of us as thought. Monsters like the Wendigo contain our deepest nightmares. They illustrate our fears in real time and in shining, blinding color. They stand as a representation of our deepest desire, ugliest pursuits, and the forbidden shadows we try to placate by slipping them into storybooks and fun caricatures.

They also allow us access to parts of the world which are taboo to believe in: ghosts and monsters can be easier to discuss over a campfire than in the office.

I could not imagine anyone else authoring these tales again other than Chad Lewis, because of his understanding of the human experience and his gift for making psychology accessible to everyone through storytelling. I feel a strong connection with this approach because psychology is how I approach the paranormal. Nothing we do or think is separate from that which is around us, it is all connected and how we tell our stories determines our reality. Everything is perception and when we understand the perception of others, we can break down fear and understand ourselves as well. Winter folklore is about the monsters in the dark, as well as our physical and emotional isolation. The winter reflects the silence so many of us fear when the noise stops; the monsters in the quiet of the woods of our minds. Folklore are stories that highlight the brightest parts of our being and darkest corners of our souls. The stories can bring lessons and light, or hell and brimstone. Nightmares are brewed in the deepest recesses of the dark, and the darkest places are often within mankind's own inner sanctums. With this understanding, Chad gives us the opportunity to explore the mysticism and magic of the winter darkness with a flashlight and an open door.

I am honored to be a small part of the enchantment that Chad imparts with every book and every legend he touches, and I promise that by the end of the last chapter, you will feel touched by a part of it as well. No matter what climate you live in, by the end of these stories, you will not just remember the folklore, you will *understand* the winter. Now, when I stand in the evergreen and ever-growing silence of the Alberta woods in deep December, I am so very conscious of the language of the legends around me and I know I am not alone.

Chad has taught me to appreciate winter in a new way: through the eyes of monsters and man, and with the elegance that only a master storyteller of humanity can tell.

—Morgan Knudsen

Table of Contents

Chapter 1
Beware The Winter Solstice

Most people know that the winter solstice is the shortest day of the year—or the longest night, depending on how you like to view it. What many people do not know is that, traditionally the solstice was thought to be one of the most powerful nights in which evil spirits and supernatural beings could come back to this realm and try to harm you. Witches, ghosts, werewolves and other menacing creatures practically had free reign to torment and devour humans under the cover of darkness. However, you do not need to despair, as there are several precautions that you can take to protect yourself from the denizens of the night during the solstice.

The darkness of the season was truly a terrifying time for early cultures as reported in the December 18, 1941, edition of the *Chicago Sentinel* which wrote, "The approach of the dark season of the year no doubt filled primitive man with dread . . . The gradual ebbing of sunlight must have filled his heart with the fear that soon the earth would be completely and forever dark." This fear of impending darkness was echoed in the October 30, 1924, edition of the *Calgary Herald*, stating, "The shortening days, lengthening nights, and increasing cold marked the temporary defeat of the sun-god and the consequent triumph of the powers of darkness."

The celebration of the solstice dates back thousands of years. Pointing to the importance of the event, the December 25, 1910, edition of the *Athens Banner* told, "The pagans looked upon this day as the turning point of nature, believing that with the lengthening of the days the renewal of life on the dead earth began." The solstice night served as a dichotomy of emotions for people—on the one hand, it was a night overrun with goblins, ghouls, and ghosts that struck fear into their hearts. Yet on the other hand, it was also the turning point towards spring and the resurrection of sunlight and life. The days leading up to the solstice were also a time of feasting and jollity as communities gathered in celebration of the upcoming turning of the season.

Traditionally, the most important precaution to take on the solstice was to have a roaring bonfire blazing throughout the night.

In addition to limiting the amount of darkness in which spirits had to hide in, fire also acted as a powerful barrier preventing any evil from attacking. Throughout the world, communities would gather around gigantic ceremonial bonfires to celebrate the important night. It was not an unusual site to see numerous blazing fires on the hilltops of cites. Today it is still advised that you keep a fire in your fireplace the whole night through. Those without a fireplace can use candles as protection, as the symbolism of light conquering dark remains the same.

One can also festoon your barn and/or the door of your house with magical plants (see the chapter on mistletoe, holly, and ivy). These evergreen plants are thought to be powerful weapons to repel evil. Horseshoes can be placed above the entrance to dwellings, to help keep witches and spirits away. Take note that the horseshoe needs to be hung with its rounded ends pointing toward the ground, or what many consider being upside down. If you have the points facing toward the sky, it is the preferred method for those looking for the horseshoe to capture good luck, but it will give you no protection against evil beings.

For those of you who are actively pursuing the paranormal though ghost hunting or monster expeditions, you may want to circle the winter solstice date on your calendar as a most opportune time to set out in pursuit of the unknown. Just make sure you avoid all of the bonfires.

4

Chapter 2
Don't Forget the Little People

Throughout history, being a farmer was a daunting proposition. The exhaustingly long days, coupled with backbreaking labor all but guaranteed that a farmer's life would be tremendously difficult. No matter how much physical and mental effort was given, it seemed as though the never-ending to-do-list remained uncompleted. These hardships were one of the main reasons that farm families were so large—the more hands to help out with chores the better. It was not uncommon for farm couples to have eight, ten, or even a dozen or more children. Every bit of help was sorely needed and appreciated, even when that help came from supernatural sources. All across the world, various cultures believed that family farms were inhabited by the little people. Whether you call them gnomes, elves, fairies, sprites, or the hidden ones, these magical creatures would often be a welcome addition to any farm.

Often living in the barn or hayloft, these unseen little people would help with the day-to-day difficulties of running a farm. They were thought to be masterful caretakers of livestock, possessing the ability to talk with the animals and to skillfully cure nearly any of their ailments. The little people also safeguarded the crops, plants, and soil, thus dramatically increasing the chances of the farm flourishing, and the human occupants not dying of starvation. Of course, all this support and assistance was predicated on the assumption that the farmers would leave offerings to the little people as a reward for their help. Traditionally, it was during the cold winter months that the little people would come inside the human home and congregate around the family hearth seeking warmth and light. Whether it was some baked goods, sweets, fruits, candies, tobacco, or even alcohol, it was during these times that it was imperative to leave out treats for the little people. Those who foolishly ignored this custom and refused to respect the little people would suffer severe consequences. Disrespectful farmers might discover that their cows would go dry or their livestock would go lame, and their crops would fail or barely produce any food. Barns and storage areas would be in disarray, and strange accidents would increase as family members suddenly become clumsy. All of these deadly setbacks could easily be prevented with simple offerings to the little people.

Americans are not alone in their belief in the little people. In fact, most of these legends originate in Europe. Scandinavian countries have many such helpful creatures. In Sweden, one of the most popular is the Tomten, a supernatural custodian of the farm. In her lovely book, *The Tomten*, Astrid Lindgren, paints the Tomten as ancient beings that have lived in the forest long before mankind arrived, writing, "He is an old, old tomten who has seen the snow of many hundreds of winters." Their reverence for the land and ancient rituals propels them into service to mankind.

In Scandinavia, residents also keep an eye out for small gnome-like creatures called the Nisse. In their wonderful book, Nisse: *The Norwegian Nisse, Its Amazing Life and History,* authors Frid Ingulstad and Svein Solem tell of numerous types of different Nisse—from the traditional house Nisse to church Nisse, forest Nisse, barn Nisse, and several others. I find the house Nisse particularly interesting as they are said to live "up in the loft of the human's house and sleep in old shoes or in woolen mittens." Usually invisible, the Nisse help in the kitchen, perform cleaning duties, and even look after young children. Their assistance, even if it is not actually seen by the naked eye, is thought to be indispensable. While talking about the Nisse for its December 23, 1961, edition, the *Dover Daily Reporter,* wrote, "People are wont also to put a platter of rice porridge outside the kitchen door on Christmas Eve for the Nisse. The platter is licked clean by morning." Perhaps as an early warning for their readers, the *Biddeford Daily Journal* including the following warning about the Nisse in their December 24, 1884, newspaper, "Offerings of sweet porridge, cakes, beer, and other delicacies are provided specially for them; but care must be taken that this act is performed with every mark of respect, otherwise they will quickly show their displeasure." In the book *The Nisse From Timsgard,* Virginia Allen Jensen retells the story of the Nisse, claiming that the Nisse is related to the elf, goblin gnome, and dwarf, but is entirely its own creature. Whatever the creature might be, its fondness for treats and goodies is not disputed.

If we assume that these creatures are beneficial to farms across the entire planet, the question then becomes—what happens to the little people when the majority of humans no longer live on farms? Throughout history the overwhelming majority of people lived out on sprawling farms. Yet, by 1900, only about 40% of Americans were involved in farming. Today that figure is less than 1%. As more and more people have deserted the rural farm life, what happens to the little people? Do they continue to tend to the ancient land as they always have, or do they migrate to cities and towns where the people live? Obviously, this question remains unanswered. Perhaps in the future, we will have a better understanding of where the little people have decided to live. However, just to be safe I like to cover all my bases, so I suggest that when you plan to leave out some cookies for Santa, you should also remember the little people.

Chapter 3
The History of Christmas Caroling

The act of Christmas Caroling has enjoyed a resurgence in popularity in recent years as more and more people discover the joys of singing beloved Christmas carols together as a group. You may think that caroling was traditionally done to promote goodwill, holiday cheer, and a sense of belonging throughout a community, and part of the custom was certainly done for those reasons. However, like most other aspects of folklore, the tradition seems to be a hodgepodge of various other practices, and in the case of caroling, the folklore consists of much weirder traditions.

The most influential custom of caroling came from the ancient tradition of wassailing, which came in two forms. In pre-Christian times, wassailing was done from either house to house or in the orchards. Wassailing occurred during winter, usually falling somewhere between the twelve days of Christmas, although engaging in wassailing was most popular on the 12th night.

The origins of house wassailing were summed up nicely in the December 23, 1975, printing of the *Mattoon Journal Gazette* which reported, "Wintertime in olde England found the merrie Elizabethans toasting each other with mugs of hot, spicy wine from the wassail bowl. It was a custom borrowed from the Saxton who drank hearty potion amidst shouts of 'Waes Hae' -good health." Over the years, much like trick-or-treating, groups of people would go from house-to-house singing songs and offering a sip of their wassail bowl in hopes that their performance would be rewarded with even more warm spirits. In times of extreme poverty and hunger, peasants and the poor visited wealthy residents during the winter time and sang, danced, and performed for them in hopes of being given food, drink, or coin for their troubles.

An even more popular (and bizarre) tradition was that of orchard wassailing. Revelers would partake in drinking spiked cider as they headed out at night to the orchards. Once among the trees of the orchard, they would choose a few of the most important and significant trees and begin sprinkling cider and other liquors over the roots to serve as an offering. The party would form a circle around a tree and begin singing traditional winter orchard songs. Consider this charming rhyme which was published in the September 12, 1903, edition of the *Elkton Cecil Whig:*

> Wassail the trees and they will beare
> You many a plum and many a peare
> For more or less fruits they will bring
> As you do give them wassailing

Since the orchards were thought to be perfect hiding places for evil spirits and supernatural beings, the louder the ceremony was, the more likely it was to scare away such demons. In his book, *The Book of Christmas Folklore*, Tristram P. Coffin expanded on how the evil spirits would be dispersed, writing. "Terrorizing evil spirits was made by firing a gun, by blowing a bullhorn, or by shouting." Amazingly, shooting their guns directly into the branches of the trees was the preferred way to expel any sinister beings from the orchard.

After completing all of the songs and overall loud racket of the shouting and shooting, sticks were wacked against the trunk of the trees in hopes of waking them up so they could get to work on producing a record crop of fruit for the following spring and summer. Since this was also the perfect time to prune fruit trees, the wassailing of orchards quickly gained popularity. Having bonfires in the orchards also played a vital role in wassailing. Not only did the fire add warmth to the celebration, more importantly, the fire aided in the banishment of evil spirits. As an additional bonus, the leftover fire ash was used to help fertilize the trees.

Throughout the decades wassailing faded in practice throughout Europe. In America the more streamlined idea of wassailing came in the form of Christmas caroling. This tradition took root and exploded in popularity during the 1920s as evidenced by a November 28, 1924, article in the *Winslow Mail* that read, "Like a snowball, the total number of American cities that have held outdoor Christmas caroling has increased from 30 in 1918 to an aggregate of 2,203 different places." A possible explanation to this rapid growth was presented in the December 10, 1927, edition of the *Saturday Spectator* which opined, "Out of the artificiality we have made of Christmas, with its 'exchanging' of gifts, there are some who are trying to re-awaken the real Christmas spirit as it has come down to us in the custom of carol singing."

In today's more modern Christmas caroling, many of the eccentric parts of traditional wassailing (shooting at evil spirits) have been discarded, and the tradition has transformed from a drunken revelry, to what many would consider a more wholesome activity of singing carols with friends and family. However, I am glad to note that people are beginning to rediscover the ancient tradition of wassailing, and have taken great joy in performing the ceremonies as they were originally meant to be, warts and all. Tons of wassail recipes exist online, allowing you to make your own spiked cider. Regardless of how you decide to celebrate the tradition, just be sure that no supernatural beings are left behind.

Chapter 4
Telling Ghost Stories by the Fire

Without a doubt one of my favorite traditions of the winter season is the long-practiced ritual of telling ghost stories by the fire. As I mentioned in the introduction, for far too long people have closely associated Halloween with all things scary. However, when you stop to consider that winter comprises all the core elements needed to create the perfect creepy season for ghost stories, Halloween takes a back seat. Remember, one of the most famous Christmas stories, *A Christmas Carol,* is actually a ghost story with Scrooge being visited by three spirits and Marley.

First of all, Christmas time is dark, very dark. The winter season brings with it cloudy days and ever-lengthening nights. Back in a time when homes were lit by candles or even lanterns, they were dimly-lit, shadowy boxes of fear. As vicious outside winds howled through gaps in the walls, as the boards creaked and groaned from the battering of the cold, the normally comfortable abode turned into a living nightmare. Once darkness crept in for the day, life in the pioneer home slowed to a crawl. The family gathered around the fire for warmth and light. Perhaps the women sewed or knitted, the men mended their tools as they partook in a tobacco pipe. Reading helped to pass the time, and on special occasions, instruments would ring music throughout the home. With our rose-colored glasses, this scenario may seem idyllic, but for the early peoples it was also a perfect time to engage in telling scary ghost tales while fortified by the safety of the fireplace.

While telling ghostly tales was extremely popular throughout the entire winter season, for many, the penultimate time for ghost and goblin tales was on Christmas Eve. In his 1891 collection of stories titled *Told After Supper*, Jerome K. Jerome wrote that nothing "satisfies us on Christmas Eve but to hear each other tell authentic anecdotes about specters." Why has Christmas Eve landed as the best time to tell spooky stories? The answer is simple—Christmas Eve was long thought to be the one day that witches, ghosts, ghouls, and monsters could not come and attack you. In essence, Christmas Eve gave you a free pass to explore as many scary topics as you wanted without the fear of retaliation from said spirits. This very belief was explained by a December 23, 1904, article in the *Olympia Washington Standard* that stated, "There were people in olden days who believed that neither ghosts nor witches dare show themselves on Christmas Eve." Even though you were safe from supernatural predators, that didn't mean you will scot-free from other troubles.

My favorite twist on the telling of ghost tales involves the idea that as everyone gathered around the fire listening to these chilling tales, if the fire cast your shadow against a wall without a head, it meant that the Grim Reaper was coming for you. This belief was covered by Tristram Coffin where he wrote about the burning of the Yule Log in his book, *The Book of Christmas Folklore,* claiming, "There it was burned, as people told ghost stories and tales of olden times, drank cider, and watched their shadows on the wall, knowing those without a head would be dead within the year." I can just imagine a family repeatedly repositioning themselves so that everyone's head could be seen in their shadows. A Christmas Day article in the 1932 edition of the *Sunday News Sun* expanded on this superstition, writing, "When lights are brought into the house on Christmas Eve if any one's shadow has no head, he will die before the end of the year and if the shadow has half a head he will die in the second half." A gloomy prediction, but I guess that living half to the second half of the year was better than the first half.

Magazines from the 1800s and early 1900s filled their winter editions with chilling ghost stories, knowing that their customers would be all too happy to find a new tale to frighten their families with. Newspapers followed suit. For its December 19, 1901, edition the *Boston Post* ran the imaginative title, "The Christmas Ghost Story." As the years progressed, this tradition lost steam and began to fade out. The Dec 24, 1919 edition of the *New Castle* opined perfectly about the decline of the Christmas ghost tale, writing, "There was a time when a Christmas wasn't a Christmas unless we could open a story book and read of December apparitions haunting the abandoned homestead. Modern conveniences, however, have legislated the Christmas ghost story out of existence."

Hold your horses newspapers, because today the tradition of telling ghost stories at Christmas has made a huge resurgence among the general public who are craving to add some semblance of history, meaning, and purpose to the modern Christmas season—one that feels as though it has been commercialized beyond all recognition. Numerous short ghost stories from the Victorian era have been published in small booklets meant to be read aloud during the Christmas season. It is great to think that even in today's fully modern, highly electronic based world, we can still all gather around the fire and settle into a scary ghost story while listening to the wind howling outside and wonder if that truly was the wind that was howling.

Chapter 5
The Magic of Mistletoe,
Holly, and Ivy

Imagine walking through the forest in winter and seeing all the plants, crops, and leaves shriveled up and wilted, dead in the icy clutches of the cold. Then off in the distance your eye catches the faintest glimpse of color peeking up through the patch of snow. Against all odds these plants have bested winter's deadly hand, and are actually thriving. One couldn't help but wonder what special properties these enchanted plants contained. The idea that holly, ivy and mistletoe possessed magical powers remains heavily entrenched in our history. Traditionally, these plants would be adorned over the entrance to your home, barn, and any other structure that needed protection from the demons in the dark.

In the old days, when superstitions ruled, these plants were thought to protect citizens from all sorts of evil spirits, demons, supernatural beings, and witches that always seemed to be lurking in every darkened corner of winter. Pagans, who lived in constant fear of evil spirits, swore by the belief that the plants had protective powers to ward off all evil that preyed on people during the darkest times of the year. The ease in which the plants could be twisted and maneuvered into wreaths and other decorations only made them more appealing. For their December 1 issue of 1907, *The Old Ladies Journal* told of this paranormal belief: "In olden days a branch of holly picked on Christmas Eve was considered a charm against witches and evil spells." The protective powers of the plants are not limited to humans; one of the weirdest legends of ivy told of feeding livestock a bit of ivy on Christmas Day in order to ward off evil spirits throughout the new year. Even the prickliness of the plants is thought to act as a barrier between you and evil.

If you do decide to use these plants to ward off evil spirits, make sure you have your timing down, It is generally believed that if you bring these charmed plants inside your home before Christmas Eve, you will only bring about misfortune to yourself and your loved ones. However, having the plants as an outdoor protection comes with no such strict calendar. As good as the plants are at deterring ghosts and ghouls, they are even better at protecting you from more mundane earthly problems. The December 24, 1941, issue of the *Marshfield News* reported "Only happiness can enter under mistletoe." A fascinating article in the 1881 Christmas edition of the *Philadelphia Times* told of the numerous curative properties of mistletoe, writing, "It was considered a sovereign remedy for epilepsy, and an antidote to poisons." Mistletoe could prevent nightmares and ensure crops would not fail. Holly could protect occupants of the home from terrible weather—including thunder and lightning. Holly also is thought to be a favorite of the forest fairies. In the December 21, 1929, edition of the paper, the *Galveston Tribune* told of an even more bizarre ritual where "The faces of babies in India and Persia are sometimes washed in the liquid in which holly bark has been soaked as a charm against evil spirits."

Today, if you mention mistletoe to anyone, odds are they will tell you about the long-practiced custom of kissing under it. Like much of folklore in general, the origin of this belief is composed of numerous bits and pieces from many other traditions and beliefs. One of various benefits of the green plants was the belief that they not only represented fertility, but were also the living symbol of it. Because the plants did not succumb to winter, they were also seen as representing everlasting life. Many scholars believe that this fertility belief played an important role in why we now practice the custom of kissing under the mistletoe. For its December 24,

1950, edition, the *Ardmore Daily Ardmoreite* wrote of this lovely tradition, "As it hangs upon the chandelier or in the doorway each lad may claim a kiss from the maid who chances beneath it and give her a pearly berry as a token of good luck. When all the berries are picked, the privilege is supposed to cease." Mistletoe also was deemed to be a predictor of future romantic happiness as evidenced by an interesting article in the December 23, 1901, edition of the *Pittston Gazette* stating, "In this country two mistletoe leaves are placed together before the fire by many an anxious lover. He or she names the leaves secretly. If they fly together as they grow crisp, those they represent will wed, or if they fly apart fate wills other-wise." In a very old superstition, it was believed that if you used more ivy than holly in the Christmas decorations, the wife would then "wear the breeches" for the following year. Other folktales told that if the holly brought in for the season was pricky (he holly), the husband would be the master of the home for the year. Conversely, if the holly was smooth (she holly), the wife would run the house. To confuse matters even more, ivy has long been thought to be a symbol of womanhood, and if it was properly placed with the symbol of man (holly), it would bring balance to a home.

Although these green plants were originally used during the winter solstice for hundreds of years, in more recent times they became commonly associated with Christmas and Jesus. On December 24, 1941, the *Mansfield News Journal* shared the enthralling belief that "Holly is also associated with Christ. According to a very old tradition, it composed the crown of thorns which he wore and drops of blood were formed into little red berries." Ivy needs something to cling onto in order to survive, a not-so-subtle allegory that humans need to cling to God in order to enjoy the afterlife.

Holiday scholars also tend to believe that the red and green of the plants and berries played a significant role in our current association with the colors of red and green as being Christmas colors. Contrary to what the popular Christmas carol would have you believe, most people today readily point to red and green, not silver and gold, as their preferred colors of Christmas. With so many curative powers attached to them, both physical and spiritual, it is no wonder that these plants have become a favorite decoration for so many. However, you would be wise to keep in mind that whichever way you choose to display your plants, just make sure that when you are finished with them, you do not just discard them in the trash or compost pile. These magical plants need to be burned to ashes, lest you be cursed with bad luck.

Chapter 6
Why We Decorate Christmas Trees

In today's world, we tend to take for granted the idea that people have always practiced the wonderful custom of bringing in a tree from the outside and decorating it with lights and ornaments. However, what you will see in this chapter is that it took a very long time for tree decorating to reach th1e wildly popular heights that it enjoys today

Throughout history, peoples from around the world have been adoring various outdoor evergreen trees. Since factory made ornaments and electric lights are relatively modern inventions, the earliest trees were festooned with fruits, nuts, and plants, including mistletoe, holly, ivy, and hay. Many cultures incorporated decorated outdoor trees into their winter festivals, rituals, and celebrations. The December 24, 1959, edition of the *Heppner Gazette Times* described the decorating of trees as "A custom of heathen origin—an offering of winter hospitality to the spirits and fairies who haunted the leafless woods." Sheryl Ann Karas, in her book *The Solstice Evergreen: The History, Folklore and Origins of the Christmas Tree* spoke of the importance of the evergreen, writing, "Where evergreens were abundant, they became the trees most highly revered, because while other trees lost their leaves and seemed to die . . . the evergreens stayed fresh and green through the most severe weather." For their Christmas Eve paper of 1945, the *Oxnard Press Courier* gave this history lesson, "Pre-Christmas Romans ornamented their homes with green boughs and bowers for the Feast of Saturnalia. . . . Druids gathered mistletoe for that season, while ancient Saxons used holly, ivy and hay."

One main purpose of these above-mentioned decorating rituals was to remind ourselves that winter was only temporary, the same reminder that was provided by the evergreen trees themselves. The decorations gave hope that light would eventually overcome darkness and life would inevitably return in the spring. In his mind bogglingly thorough book on Christmas trees, *The Christmas Tree,* researcher Daniel J. Foley wrote, "Living plants exemplifying the essence of beauty helped to dispel the gloom of winter, and the evergreens particularly symbolized eternal life.

Adorning outdoor trees was one thing, but where did the idea of bringing the trees inside to decorate come from? As you will read in a later chapter, it was common for people to bring the Yule log into their homes, but this was done to actually burn the tree, not to adore and admire it.

The tradition of bringing trees inside and decorating them comes from Germany. Although pinpointing an exact year that the first tree was brought inside is nearly impossible, the idea originated in Germany during the 16th century. Prior to this, people had their Yule trees, an evergreen that was placed near the entrance or dooryard of a home, However, the Yule tree was not decorated, and most scholars contend that the Christmas tree is an altogether different tradition. In popular culture, many credit Martin Luther as inventing the Christmas tree. The legend tells of Martin Luther wandering home at night on a cloudless Christmas Eve when he looked up in awe at the wondrous twinkling stars in the sky. Inspired by their beauty, he went home and set up a tree for his children. He lit numerous candles on the tree in an effort to duplicate the beauty of Mother Nature. However, it should be noted that no official documentation of this story actually exists, hence it is regarded as a heartwarming legend, but certainly not fact.

Regardless of its true originator, the Christmas tree quickly caught on throughout Germany, and soon everyone seemed to be placing candles in their trees. The candles were a powerful symbol of light that was meant to scare away all the evil spirits. It is hard to over-state how important the idea of light conquering darkness was to early peoples. The Christmas tree gained such popularity that it was common in Germany to see Christmas trees placed through-out graveyards on Christmas Eve in order that the deceased could enjoy the holiday spirit as well. Remember, this was a time when evil spirits and supernatural beings were lurking everywhere, just waiting for you to let down your guard. From Germany, the tra-dition of tree decorating moved to the rest of Europe as Germans relocated to other countries and brought their treasured Christmas traditions with them. Yet, it is the German born Prince Albert who is broadly credited with bringing widespread use of the Christmas tree to England. In the 1840s, Prince Albert routinely put Christmas trees throughout Windsor Castle, and popular magazines featured drawings of the royal family gathered around a lavishly decorated Christmas tree. Common folks wanted to emulate the royal family and the tradition spread quickly through the entire country.

In America, the traditions and customs of the Christmas tree arrived here with the German immigrants, including the Pennsylvania Dutch. Eager to preserve their way of life from the old country, Germans celebrated Christmas with their beloved trees, and soon Christmas trees were all the rage in the new country. One of the most important pieces playing into the popularity of the Christmas tree came with the invention of electric lights. With this inven-tion, it was easier than ever to have beautifully lit trees, as the stringed lights easily and safely replaced the dangerous and trou-blesome candles. The addition of mass-produced ornaments set the Christmas tree custom off on a path of unprecedented popularity that continues to this very day.

Today, whether you choose to decorate an artificial tree or drag in a live evergreen, it is comforting to know that you are continuing the tradition of allowing light to not only cast out darkness, but to also ward off all of the evil creatures that hide in that darkness. Just as people have been doing for countless years, you are placing in your house a constant seasonal reminder that life will rebound and flourish in the spring. Just make sure you keep a close eye on those candles!

Chapter 7
Christmas Eve Superstitions

There are considerably more superstitions and legends involving Christmas Eve than any other time of the year, including the over-hyped Friday the 13th. Outside of the well-known traditions of leaving out cookies and milk for Santa, or hanging stockings on the mantel, Christmas Eve is bursting with a huge assortment of odd customs and beliefs.

Arguably the most important of these rituals is the act of opening your home's door or window at midnight in order to allow the Christmas season to flow in. The *Tacoma News Tribune* took it a step further in their 1972 Christmas Eve edition by advising their readers, "At midnight tonight you should open all your doors to let out the bad spirits that may be living in your house." In many regions of the world this ritual would be accompanied by saying 'Welcome Father Christmas' or 'Welcome Christmas' or some similar greeting to ensure the season's arrival.

On the same note as letting bad spirits exit your home, old tales tell that if you burn elder wood on Christmas Eve, you will have revealed to you all the witches and sorcerers of the neighborhood. Continuing with the occult theme, if you visit a crossroads between 11pm and midnight on Christmas night, you will be shown what will concern you most in the new year.

One of the weirdest Christmas Eve legends revolves around the actions of bees. In the northern portion of America, it is extremely difficult to even find bees in the winter, yet tales of them buzzing about in the Yuletide season are plentiful. Apparently, bees revel in the merriment of Christmas Eve just as much as humans do. In 1889, the *Kingwood Argus* reported that "bees sing in their hives between the 24th and 25th of December, while mysterious bells can be heard echoing underground." In her book, *Discovering Christmas Customs and Folklore*, Margaret Baker told of legends of bee hives singing during Christmas Eve, writing, "They hummed the Old Hundredth Psalm or sang a carol at midnight." In 1931, the *Des Moines Register* fascinated its readers by claiming "at midnight on Christmas eve, bees sing in their hives." Regrettably, it is not known if they actually sing the carols or simply buzz along to them like the rest of us who don't actually know the lyrics. Either way, it is still a pretty fantastic legend.

It is not just humans that are affected by Christmas Eve legends, animals tend to act a bit squirrelly during the season, too. The most popular animal legend tells that Christmas Eve is the one night in which animals are granted the power to speak. *The Tacoma News Tribune* wrote of a delightful tale that the oxen kept in the stable where Jesus was born refused to eat their evening hay, instead keeping it so it could be used as a bed at the birth of Jesus. For their reward, "the whole bovine species was granted the power of speech for one hour every Christmas Eve." Most of the explanations given for why animals are able to speak on Christmas Eve do in fact involve their species being present at the birth of the Savior. To show their gratitude for this precious gift, and to pay their respect to the birth of Jesus, it is said that many animals can be seen kneeling during Christmas Eve. I understand that it is nearly impossible to fight the temptation to eavesdrop on these animals talking, but be advised that if you do, not only will they just be talking bad about you, your nosiness will also bring you misfortune throughout the following year. A lot of dog lovers will be saddened to hear a story that appeared in the 1932 Christmas Edition of the *Sunday News* that told, "Howling dogs who did their howling on Christmas Eve were destined by olden superstition to go mad before the end of the year."

Strangely, the fear of dying is closely entwined into Christmas Eve lore. It is said that at midnight you can perform the miracle of turning water into wine (just as Jesus did), but if you are foolish enough to drink the wine, you will die. If you make a little heap of salt on the table and it melts overnight, you will die within the next year. If you sit under a pine tree on Christmas Eve you might be able to hear the wondrous sound of Angels singing—a sign that you will be seeing Angels in the next year because you will die. If you burn a candle on Christmas Eve, you should be warned—if the candle goes out—you guessed it, you will die. In the old days it was exciting to add a little danger to your rituals, which is why these are just a few of the endless ways in which you can meet your end on Christmas Eve. After taking in all of these rituals and customs, it is truly amazing that our ancestors were able to accomplish anything during the holiday season. Their days and nights would have overflowed with attempts to adhere to all these superstitions, let alone survive them.

Chapter 8
The Yule Log

Today, when most people think of the Yule Log, the first thing that pops into their head is the delicious dessert cake—not an actual log. However, the Yule Log plays a significant role in the celebration of the winter season. During the Twelve Days of Christmas (beginning on December 25 and running through January 6) it was advised that you have the Yule Log burning in your fireplace. Due to the extremely dangerous weather, and even more dangerous creatures lurking outside, the sensible choice was to remain in your home for much of the unforgiving winter season. The Yule Log fire was meant to literally bring light and warmth to the cold darkness, but on a more supernatural level the continuous fire was designed to ward off witches, demons, and evil spirits that were thought to always be lurking in the dark icy shadows.

Each country seemed to have its own preferred species of tree to be used in the ritual, although preferences often varied from region to region. Regardless of personal preferences, any tree could serve the purpose of being the Yule log. A few days before Christmas, families would venture out onto their property and chop down a tree large enough to serve their purposes. The entire process was done in a celebratory manner. The felled tree would be adorned with bells and ribbons, creating a wonderful spectacle of sight for any passing friends or neighbors. From there, it was hauled back to the house with great pomp and circumstance—thus anointing the tree with great folkloric significance. Once the log made it to the home there were several ways in which one could utilize it. One popular practice was to simply place one end of the tree into the fireplace, and as the tree burned away, you would occasionally shove more and more of the tree into the fireplace. Others would cut the tree into smaller, more manageable blocks of wood that could be added as needed. Either way, the Yule Log fire was to be started with the leftover remains from the previous year's Yule Log—which were kept throughout the year as a good luck charm. In fact, research by Andy Thomas in his book, *Christmas: A Short History from Santa to Solstice,* tells that the remnant wood could also be used to ward off "toothache and chilblains" (Chilblains-painful red rash patches on the skin after you have been in the cold). Other lore states that the charcoal from the Yule log protects the house from lightning strikes, fire, and ill-luck. It also said that it fortifies people from all sorts of various diseases.

Outside of the above-mentioned benefits, the Yule Log was also thought to spread some supernatural magic. In his wonderful book, *Christmas Miscellany,* Jonathan Green wrote about many Norse cultures' belief that "the burning Yule log warmed the frozen shades of the family's dearly departed who returned to the ancestral home every Christmas Eve." Tristram Coffin expanded on Yule Log lore in *The Book of Christmas Folklore,* writing that people would often wish upon the Yule Log. The importance of keeping the Yule Log lit for the entire Twelve Days could not be understated. Whether by neglect or accident, if the Yule log ever went out, it would bring a year full of ill-fate, misfortune, and impending doom.

Over the years, as more and more people migrated away from their traditional family farms in order to live in large cities, the impracticality of cutting down a huge tree on your property and hauling it into your home meant that burning the Yule Log for twelve days lost favor among the masses. Families began to modify the tradition and shortened the timespan of log burning from twelve days to twelve hours. Today, many factors have contributed to the further decline of ancient Yule Log tradition. First of all, a good percentage of homes no longer have a wood burning fireplace (Sad news for

Santa). Even more troubling is the overall lack of awareness of the tradition. Our hectic lifestyles have cast aside many long-held traditions and rituals. However, all is not lost, as people are starting to improvise in clever ways to ensure that the celebration of the Yule Log never becomes extinct. Those without a fireplace have turned to lighting candles for the Twelve Days, even going so far as to place the candle(s) in their sink when they leave the house to help prevent starting a house fire. Others use the eerily realistic fake candles to light their homes. The simplicity of electric and gas fireplaces is all the rage in today's modern time-pressured world, and they too are being used to celebrate the Yule Log tradition. Remember, it was the symbolism of the fire's light overcoming the darkness, and keeping evil at bay, and most importantly, inspiring everlasting faith that warmth and life would return in the spring that gave the Yule Log tradition its power—and that can never be extinguished.

Chapter 9
The History of Santa Claus

When it comes to being associated with the Christmas season, abso-
lutely nothing comes remotely close to the legend of Santa Claus.
He is hands down the most iconic representation of the holiday season. You would have a very difficult time finding someone unfamil-
iar with Santa, even among those who do not celebrate Christmas.
Known around the world as Saint Nicholas (Nick), Kris Kringle,

Jolly St. Nick, Father Christmas, Pere Noel, Kerstman, and count-less other names, Santa personifies the spirit, heart, and all that is good about the Christmas season. However, the image you have of Santa today—a jolly plump man with a long snow-white beard donned in a red suit trimmed with white fur—is not the Santa our ancestors knew and loved. Much like modern pop stars, Santa has continuously reinvented himself as he moves through the centuries.

The Santa Claus of today owes his heritage to an assortment of European legends. The lineage of Santa Claus dates back to the days of Odin, the Norse God who flew around in December's Yuletide season with his eight-legged (Santa's eight reindeer?) horse which pulled his mighty sleigh. Odin was blessed with the magical knowl-edge of knowing who had been bad and who had been good. From Odin came the legends of Europe's Father Christmas and Saint Nicolas, both of which have combined and morphed into America's modern interpretation of Santa Claus. In the old days Santa Claus was draped in various rugged animal furs and was seen more in the vein of a magical woodsman in tune with both the natural and supernatural worlds. The furred Saint Nick was routinely portrayed as a tall and gaunt man with a long white beard and his ever-present wide-brimmed hat, which incidentally was one of Odin's favorite disguises as well. Over time Santa updated his look and was often depicted donning a beautiful green or even blue furred suit. After a few additional style changes and image updates, Santa finally landed on his famous current look, the red and white suit paired with his shiny black boots. His choice of hats also morphed into the long conical stocking hat that we know so well today. Although Santa was first brought here by immigrants leaving their old countries for the New World, Santa is now as American as they come. While the rest of the world has adored him for much longer, no other country can outdo us when it comes to laying claim to Santa.

Much of what we know about Santa can be directly sourced to a poem first published anonymously in the *Troy Sentinel* on December 23, 1823, titled, "A Visit From St. Nicholas." Better known as "'Twas the Night Before Christmas," the poem established many of the most important aspects of Santa Claus. Saint Nicolas (Santa) was not portrayed as being of the average male height that we know today; instead he was described as a "jolly little elf," with "a miniature sleigh, and eight tiny rein-deer." Luckily, all of the reindeer came complete with names: Dasher, Dancer, Prancer, Vixen, Comet, Cupid, Dunder and Blixem." Obviously, the names Dunder and Blixem did not stand the test of time and were replaced with Donner and Blitzen.

Even though he is better known for a different holiday-themed book (*The Legend of Sleepy Hollow*) in the early 1800s, author Washington Irving also played a large role in introducing Santa to American audiences. In his *Knickerbocker's History of New York*, Irving wrote of Saint Nicholas (Santa) riding over the rooftops of houses and coming inside to smoke his pipe.

Believe it or not, Santa's early American origin was used in overtly political ways. Some forty years after the above-mentioned poem was published, in the height of the Civil War, *Harper's Weekly* published an illustration by Thomas Nast in its January 1863 magazine which continued the jolly little elf interpretation of Santa. In the drawing Santa is cloaked in a stars and stripes shirt while busily dazzling a crowd of Union Soldiers by maneuvering a marionette in the likeness of a Confederate officer, the image clearly portraying Santa as a Union supporter. Over the next two decades, dozens of Nast's illustrations of Santa were published around the world, forever linking the artist to the magical elf.

Even though Thomas Nast was first, perhaps no other artist played a greater role in the shaping of the modern Santa than illustrator Haddon Sundblom. Many people erroneously believe that the Coca-Cola (Coke) Company was responsible for choosing Santa's red and white uniform in order to slyly match the brand colors of their popular soda pop. The real story of Coke's association with Santa had nothing to do with spreading generosity and goodwill—it involved only one thing—money. In 1931, looking to boost dismal winter sales, which dropped off every year with the retreat of summer's heat, Coca-Cola hired Sundblom to create some Christmas advertisements featuring Santa. As you previously read, up until this point, Santa was often depicted as wearing several different colored outfits, including the traditional red and white. Seizing on the perfect union of the company's brand colors and Santa's red and white suit, Sundblom ran with the idea. His version of Santa was one of a heavier, more wholesome, jovial white-bearded man with a twinkle in his eye. The pairing was so successful that Sundblom's interpretation of Santa still remains the most loved and recognized version of old St. Nick.

Another more modern modification of Santa arrived in the removal of Santa's beloved pipe. Early illustrations of Santa routinely showed him with a tobacco pipe peeking out from his bearded mouth. Until fairly recently, the idea of Santa enjoying his pipe while visiting children was not deemed to be anything out of the ordinary. Today, however, much like the general public, Santa seems to have learned of the dangers of tobacco and has wisely put an end to his smoking habit. Contrary to the free-wheeling old days, one would now be hard pressed to find a single current image of Santa smoking.

I find it fascinating that Santa gained mainstream prominence in the US during the Civil War, when the country was deeply divided over political beliefs, a fact that is not lost on me as I write this chapter in the fall of 2022, when it seems like our country is as politically divided as ever. To me, this illustrates the salient importance of the legend of Santa. Perhaps the symbolism of Santa spreading love, selfless giving, and a sense of belonging is needed more today than ever before.

Chapter 10
The Deadly Wendigo

Wendigo. The mere mention of these monsters' names was enough to strike absolute terror, chaos, and panic into the very fabric of early First Nation life, often forcing peoples to abandon their communities until the deadly beasts had passed. For hundreds of years, Wendigos have been the most frightening things ever to set foot in North America.

Born from the legends of First Nation peoples in Canada, the terrifying legend quickly spread to the Great Lakes and Northeastern regions of the United States. The tale of the Wendigo is both cautionary and horrifying. Traditional descriptions of the Wendigo tell of a dreadful looking creature that is extremely tall and lanky and whose body is twisted and withered in muscle-deprived bone. Its discolored skin is covered in filthy spotted patches of hair covered with the remnants of its unspeakable acts. Many times, the Wendigo is seen with no mouth or lips—due to its insatiable hunger when no prey (humans) is around, it resorts to consuming its own body. Many consider the Wendigo as the embodiment of winter. When food is scarce and game is nowhere to be found, people are starving and are at their weakest—mentally, physically, and spiritually—this is when the Wendigo is at its most powerful.

The Wendigo could show up in two forms. In its physical form, it was gigantic, appearing to be somewhere between eight-feet-tall and as large as it wanted to be. Its voice could paralyze you with fear, thus making it even easier for the monster to hunt you down and devour you. Perhaps ever scarier than its physical form, the Wendigo could arrive in spirit form and possess you, slowly turning you into a Wendigo. Those who believed they were "turning Wendigo" would often sit alone listlessly staring off into the distance. They were lethargic, weary, depressed, appearing as though they were trapped in some dream-like stupor that they could not awaken from. They would purposefully isolate themselves from the others, refusing to eat anything and rarely speaking to another person. Even more troubling is the fact that when they did talk, they insisted that their loved ones have transformed into delicious looking game animals like moose and beaver. Eventually, the excruciating pain set in and they complained that ice was beginning to build up inside of their bodies. At night, they wailed, writhed, and screamed out that they were going to turn into a Wendigo and kill and devour everyone in sight. We have dozens and dozens of cases where people killed someone because they suspected that person was turning into a Wendigo. In fact, many of those unfortunate souls who believed they were turning into a Wendigo begged to be killed before it was too late and they hunted and devoured their loved ones.

Without a doubt, the most infamous case of a Wendigo revolves around the gruesome tale of a man named Swift Runner. In the harsh winter of 1878-79 Swift Runner, a Cree Indian living in the heavily forested Athabasca region of Alberta, Canada, went crazy and killed and consumed his entire family (wife and six children). The following spring Swift Runner was captured and arrested for his dastardly crimes. During his trial, Swift Runner claimed he had been possessed by the Wendigo and had his humanity stripped from him by the deadly monster. The sensational and gory case made international news as Swift Runner met his fate as he hanged from the gallows.

Just in case you thought the Wendigo was simply a superstition from the past, consider that in the fall of 2018, as part of the Travel Channel's *In Search of Monsters* episode on the Wendigo, I traveled to the Northwoods of Spooner, Wisconsin, to interview Justice and John, two young teenage brothers who believed they both had separate encounters with a Wendigo-like creature while away at summer camp. Positioned deep in the woods, the camp's sparse buildings and dilapidated-looking cabins stick out from the landscape, appearing like a strange lumberjack camp from the 1920s that time had forgotten. The whole area exuded a dark evil creepiness that permeated the crisp damp air. The entire camp layout looked like some discarded horror movie set. Even though I truly love historical buildings, especially authentically rustic ones, I couldn't believe that any modern-day parent would shuttle their kids off to this camp.

It was just two years prior to our interview that the young brothers found themselves enrolled in the summer camp. Justice, the older brother, was in his cabin one night enjoying a game of cards with his buddy when suddenly his eyes were attracted to the window by two white lights flickering bright in the night air. At first glance, Justice thought the lights were nothing more than a moth, but as he took a closer look, he noticed that the lights were actually the eyes of some tall odd-looking creature that seemed to be crouched over and peering through the window. Amazingly, Justice locked eyes with the fearsome creature for about five seconds before it swiftly darted out of sight. Justice told me that "it was definitely something I hadn't seen before; it was humanoid, but it wasn't human." The entire incident left him with the eerie impression that whatever the thing was . . .it was evil and out hunting for victims!

Although Justice had his sighting through the window of his presumably safe cabin, his younger brother wasn't nearly so lucky. Just one night after Justice had his sighting, John and a friend were wandering towards their cabin (a different cabin) to grab some sweatshirts to ward off the chilly night air. As they got near the lodging John stopped dead in his tracks at the sight of a seven-foot creature standing in the woods. The monster, which John described to me as looking like, "A normal person walking down the street except he had longer legs, longer arms, very tall, and was pitch black." John was adamant that the creature wasn't just a person prowling about in the woods—instead, it was something he had certainly never seen before. When John and his friend had first approached, the bone-thin creature appeared to be bracing itself against a tree, but when the twosome walked a bit closer, the thing removed its hand from the tree and became very agitated. Petrified, intimidated, and fearing that the beast was out for blood, John and his friend instinctively started backing away from the monster only to discover that the beast was now moving toward them—so they "ran like no other."

Over the last twenty-five plus years I have received many reports from those who believed they had encountered the Wendigo. The locations of the sightings vary widely from Canada to Wisconsin to South Dakota and beyond. These sightings illustrate the continuing belief that the Wendigo is not simply a nearly forgotten relic of history.

Chapter 11
Krampus: The Demon of Christmas

In America, the worst thing that will happen to misbehaved and naughty children is that Santa Claus will place coal in their stockings—which in the old days would have been a good thing as you could burn the coal to heat your home. However, Europeans approached the holiday season a little differently. They were not playing around; if an obstinate child was not on their best behavior throughout the year, they would get an unwelcome visit from a Yule-time demon named Krampus.

The mere sight of Krampus is enough to strike overwhelming fear in the bravest of souls. Looking like some sort of demon goat, this winter monstrosity is covered in dark hair/fur that runs over its distorted body. Perched on cloven hoofs, this intimidating beast has gigantic horns springing from his hideous head. Complete with a creepy tail and a grotesquely long red tongue slithering out from his fanged teeth, Krampus is the embodiment of evil. To make matters worse, Krampus carries with him a wicked switch (usually made of birch) that is used to dole out punishment. On his back, he wears a well-worn woven basket that allows him to carry around his victims.

There is some debate over the exact origins of Krampus. Like a lot of folklore, exactness in the legend of Krampus is extremely difficult to ascertain. Many scholars tend to agree that Krampus arose from Slovak and Austrian regions which held celebrations for the satanic-looking beast. Reports of these festivals were not officially recorded until the mid-1500s. Just how far back the idea goes of a winter monster rebelling against proper traditions remains unknown. In many regions throughout Europe, on the evening of December 5 (Krampusnacht) Krampus is said to accompany Saint

Nicholas as the Jolly Saint travels from house to house giving out gifts, nuts, sweets, and candies to all the deserving boys and girls. His righthand man (demon) is Krampus, whose job it is to punish the ill-behaved children—kids that were naïve enough to believe that Krampus would not make them pay for their actions. Usually, it only took a couple of swift whips of the switch to put the screaming children back on the right track. If a kid had been particularly wicked, Krampus would toss them in his basket and drag them to Hell, or to his hidden lair where he would kill or devour them—either way they would never be seen or heard from again. In 1903, the *Mayville Daily Appeal* put a nice twist on the fate of the abducted children, writing about Krampus, "His work was to carry off bad children in a big basket, to feed them to the bears in the wilderness."

Over the years, the legends of St. Nick and Krampus became intertwined and have been linked as some sort of Ying/Yang of Christmas, Nicholas fulfilling the role of saint and Krampus serving as a representative of evil. In 1872, while writing about Christmas legends in its December 23 edition, the *Detroit Free Press*, stated that Saint Nicholas was "followed by a masked servant called Krampus." This article would be reprinted every December throughout various US newspapers for several decades. In 1889, the December 22 edition of the *Philadelphia Times* further linked the two Christmas visitors, reporting that Saint Nicholas rewarded good children, "but naughty children the good saint passed sorrowfully by, and the dreadful, horned 'Krampus' (hobgoblin) creeps up to the bedside and lays a long switch on the shoe." In 1891, the *Bury and Norwich Post,* explored various St. Nick legends from around the world for its Dec. 22 edition. When it came to St. Nick's companion in Austria, the paper wrote, "It is the frightful Krampus with his clanking chains and horrible devil's mask, who, notwithstanding his gilded nuts and apples, gingerbread and toys, which he carries in his basket, is the terror of young folks."

A fascinating twist on the idea that Krampus was nothing more than a fear-inducing bogeyman came in the form of a December 5 (Krampusnacht) article from 1903, published in the *Manchester Evening News*, that read, "In Austria, too, Santa Claus is supposed to bring a saintly figure of himself to good children, while the naughty he gives a demon of Krampus. But such is the depravity of human nature that many boys and girls prefer to get a Krampus. Saints and angels are good and prosaic, but the toy imps are delightfully grotesque." It is interesting to read this article today, knowing that its author never could have imagined the heights of popularity that the "delightfully grotesque" Krampus would enjoy in today's world.

One odd tradition that sprung up around Krampus was the act of people sending one another Krampus-themed holiday cards. In the late 1800s and throughout the 1900s, holiday-themed Krampus postcards were all the rage. People would send out a postcard with a depiction of Krampus punishing a child to all of their friends and family with the inscription of "Greetings from Krampus." Even more bizarre were the postcards in which Krampus was involved with scantily clad females—his long red tongue an obvious phallic symbol. The weirder and more sinister the images were, the more popular the card was. I am happy to say that sending a Krampus postcard is a tradition that I continue to practice to this very day, as each year many of my friends and family members are probably not too happy to receive a scary Krampus card from me.

Today, the legend of Krampus is more popular and celebrated than ever before. As Christmas time has become more commercialized. People have become disillusioned with ever-increasing price tags that the season carries. People are hungry for meaning and tradition to be injected back into the holiday season. People are seeking an anti-establishment anti-hero, and Krampus with its long history of bucking the holiday cheer fits that mold perfectly. Pop culture is filled with references to Krampus, from numerous horror movies, to the TV show *Grimm;* even Scooby Doo got to experience Krampus in an episode of *Mystery Incorporated.* In today's hectic and often demoralizing world, we need the goodness of Santa Claus more than even, but paradoxically, we need the counterbalance of evil Krampus just as much.

Chapter 12
Watch Out for Belsnickel

To avoid religious persecution, those in German speaking areas of Europe left behind their homelands in hopes of a better life and more freedoms in the new land of America. During the arduous voyage, they brought what little personal possessions they could, along with their language, religious beliefs, customs, and rituals. Beyond this, they also brought along the Belsnickel. Folklore creatures are never bound to one area or region; they exist outside of geography, they thrive among the peoples who believe in them, who fear them, who pass legends of them from one generation to the next—they exist regardless of where people choose to reside. Today, known as the Pennsylvania Dutch, these people gave Belsnickel a comfortable new home in the U.S.in which to frighten all.

Physically, Belsnickel (Nicholas in furs) casts an intimidating and frightening presence. Decked out in long flowing tattered-up furs and rags, he resembles an evil disheveled-looking beast straight out of the woods—vaguely human, yet also part something else, something that is not easily categorized. In his hand he holds a hefty-looking switch that he effortlessly uses on any deserving soul. Similar to how Santa Claus keeps a list of who has been naughty or nice, Belsnickle's job is to make sure that children mind their parents and continue to work on their good behavior. However, instead of just rewarding those who walk a straight line, Belsnickel prefers to punish those foolish enough to consider him nothing more than a silly superstition.

On Christmas Eve (or a few nights before), long before Santa pays a visit, Belsnickel gleefully makes his sinister way from home to home in search of those whose need punishment. Children nervously listen for any sounds of crunching footsteps in the snow while their tiny faces are glued to the windows. Belsnickel is coming. On the nights leading up to Christmas, parents that are dealing with any children resisting bedtime only need to allude to hearing eerie footsteps coming from outside the child's window, because the specter of Belsnickel prowling about the yard was more than enough to calm the most rambunctious of children. Belsnickel is coming.

Upon his dreaded arrival, Belsnickel unnervingly announces his arrival by slowly scratching his switch against your window before tapping his long filthy fingernails on the glass and as he demands entrance. In 1929, for its Christmas Eve article, the *Lancaster New Era*, told of the life-altering horror that Belsnickel brought, writing, "There are today middle-aged Lancastrians, brought up in the country, who can recall their fear of Belsnickel's visit." Upon gaining entrance to your dwelling, his thunderous voice would inquire as to who has been naughty and who had been nice. Those who didn't go completely silent with fear bravely pleaded their cases with the otherworldly-looking monster. What happened next was covered in 1932 in the December 21 edition of the *Latrobe Bulletin*, "After he questioned them, he would throw nuts all over the floor, then as they scrambled to gather them, Belsnickel started work with the switch." Those children who were privy to previous bouts of Belsnickel's switch cleverly waited for his departure before daring to scoop up their delicious delights. Later that evening, after their fear and terror had partially subsided, kids would fall fast asleep with hopes of a visit from the more tolerant and loving Santa Claus.

In the early to mid-1900s, Belsnickel's image began to soften within communities that felt his trusty switch was overused, and feared perhaps his image was a tad too disturbing. Instead of frightening children into compliance as he had always done, Belsnickel's more caring side was pushed to the forefront as evidenced by the 1933 article from the *Buffalo Evening News* which wrote. "He'll call a cheery greeting to the householder and welcomed, he'll warm himself by the fireside, while the family gathers 'round. He'll be carrying the same 'switch,' but there will be a twinkle in his eye."

Thankfully, the amelioration of Belsnickel did not stick. Today, Belsnickel is celebrated in the same manner as he was originally meant to be, painful switch and all. I think the *Times Argus* summed it up perfectly in its December 13, 1981, edition by opining on the significance of Belsnickel: "The modus operandi of Belsnickel was calculated to accomplish two things—to warn of punishment and to offer a taste of reward. He was a magical figure, conjuring up the deep-seated feeling that someone, somewhere, keeps a little black book in which all of our deeds, good or bad, are entered." I take great comfort in today's resurgence of interest in the Belsnickel legend. I hope that he continues to thrive and sticks around to terrorize many future generations of Americans.

Chapter 13
The Twelve Days of Christmas

Thanks in large part to the perennially popular carol, hearing about the Twelve Days of Christmas elicits visions of turtle doves, French hens, and a partridge in a pear tree. We imagine with rose-colored glasses that these days are filled with beautiful sleigh rides over a fresh blanket of pure white snow as chestnuts roast over an open fire nearby. Yet, in reality, the Twelve Days were filled with dark and scary superstitions telling of werewolves, demons, ghosts, and never-ending bad omens.

It was generally considered bad luck to have been born during the Twelve Days of Christmas (December 25-January 6). Most of the explanations revolve around the fact that if you were born during this time, you were drawing attention away from the birth of the Savior. Even though most scholars agree that Jesus was most likely not born in December, the ill-fated legends stuck and the folkloric beliefs continue to this day. In 1873, if you opened up the January 20 edition of the *Cincinnati Commercial* newspaper you would have read this warning about the Twelve Nights: "All infernal, limboed, or otherwise uncanny spirits are abroad in unwonted power." The article touched upon another interesting piece of folklore. "Olaf's werewolves are abound in those nights, too." Not only were werewolves thought to be plentiful in the forests and orchards. old superstitions tell that any poor soul who was unfortunate enough to be born during the Twelve Days had a good chance of turning into a werewolf. You have to keep in mind that during much of our history, werewolves were considered to be all too real, and the mere mention of them terrified the general public as werewolves were held in the same dreadful light as other denizens of the dark.

Being born on Christmas Day served as a double-edged sword. On the one hand, those born on Christmas Day were looked upon as possessing all sorts of magical powers. In 1920, the December 22 edition of *Buffalo Evening News* shared numerous superstitions for those born on the wrong date, including the belief that "they have the power of healing by 'laying on of the hands' and of second sight." The *Kerrville Mountain Sun* wrote "those born on Christmas Day have the power to see spirits and even to command them to their bidding." However, babies born during "sermon time" on Christmas Eve portend a death in the household. Even with all the strange beliefs, it was a considerably better omen to be born on Christmas Day, than to perish on it. Dying on Christmas Day was thought to be an ill-omen when it came to the question of where you would spend eternity in the afterlife.

Almost as though it is setting up a bad Hollywood sequel of bad things happening next year, the last night of the twelve nights might just be the scariest. In 1906, an article in the *New York Times* covered a ton of holiday folklore, and when it came to the Twelfth Night, this is what they wrote: "On Twelfth Night or 'Hogmany' the air was supposed to swarm with witches. The protecting fire (see Yule Log) must burn all night, and no strange person or animal must be let into the house, lest a demon should enter in disguise." This might be my favorite piece of folklore in this entire book. Just imagine sitting in the early afternoon darkness of your home, barely lit by candles and lanterns as the cold blistering winds howl outside as you are deadly afraid of any knock on the front door, believing that demons were trying to invade your home.

Chapter 14
New Year's Eve Superstitions

Forget everything you know about New Year's Eve celebrations—including the dropping of the Times Square ball, the funny hats and noisemakers, and kissing someone at midnight, because the old folklore surrounding the new year is much creepier and weirder than you could ever imagine.

Many pose the question, "Why were people so wary of the turning of the new year?" One good answer came in 1922 when the *Ephraim Enterprise* wrote, "Midnight on New Year's Eve was always considered a time of special activity for the spirits of evil. In order to overcome them holier and more powerful influences had to be invoked. The *Elizabethtown Chronicle* added to the legend, writing in 1943, "Midnight on New Year's Eve was considered a very auspicious time for the spirits of evil. The evil spirits, or genii could be overcome only by holy appeal to the good genii. Often food was left outside of the houses to pacify the evil spirits and induce them to pass by without doing any harm." Leaving food out on New Year's Eve so demonic spirits don't invade your house? Once again winter rituals surpass Halloween in their overall creepiness.

Similar to Christmas Eve, one of the most vital things to do on New Year's Eve is to open a door or window at midnight, not just to allow the new year easy entrance, but even more importantly, to allow the previous year a path to leave. The ritual allows for health and prosperity to reside in your home for the coming year while sweeping away all the negative aspects of the previous twelve months. Once the doors and windows had been opened, families could seek out the next important step—the "First-Footer." The first footer was to be the first person to enter the home after the strike of midnight. It was of utmost importance that this person be a man as explained by the December 28, 1936 edition of the *Midland Daily Telegraph,* "On no account must a woman be the first to cross a threshold, else the luck of the house would be ill indeed." The important visitor would often bring with them gifts of coal, fruits, nuts, or drinks to help ensure good luck. Sometimes this crucial role was given to a professional who charged a fee as they made their way from home to home.

The fear of death was unrelenting in the old days. A majority of these New Year's Eve rituals were completed with the expectation of warding off the Grim Reaper. In 1879, the *Birmingham Daily Post* perfectly captured the anxiety and fear that permeated the season, writing, "New Year's Eve superstitions take the form of omens or auguries foretelling joy or sorrow, prosperity or disaster in the coming year." If any candle or lamp were taken outside the home on New Year's Day, it meant some member of the family would die before the new year was over. Likewise, one odd belief tied to both death and the New Year was covered on December 31, 1901, by the *Gloucestershire Echo,* which told that on New Year's Eve "in many cottages it is customary for the housewife, after raking the fire for the night, to spread the ashes smoothly over the floor with the tongs, in expectation of finding the next morning the print of a foot." If the toe of the print pointed towards the door, it was firmly believed that death would find one member of the family. If, however, the toe pointed inwards, it signaled the impending arrival of a new family member.

Bonfires are an integral part of the New Year's Eve tradition. On this night cities would light up against the dark night sky as humongous community-wide fires erupted alongside smaller, more manageable family fires that littered the countryside. In 1930, the *Derby Daily*

Telegraph claimed that "Throughout Scotland, festive bonfires will blaze on village greens." The *St Louis Globe Democrat* explained the importance of such fires writing, "They intend these fires to both light the spirit of the old year on its passage and to greet with cheerful welcome the coming of the new." By burning off the old year, the fire also cleansed the incoming year. In many instances, the bonfires were accompanied by the blasting of guns in an effort to "murder" the previous year, thus making it easier for the new year to arrive. The "murdering" of the old year was heavily symbolic, but along with the roaring fire, the noise from the discharge of the weapon was also believed to scare away any evil spirits or creatures lurking in the nearby darkness. As the joyous imbibing of alcohol progressed, the addition of fireworks and explosives gave revelers the sense that evil was retreating.

By far one of the weirdest New Year rituals was covered in the December 23, 1906, edition of the *New York Times* where it was reported in many rural areas the odd custom was to "be smoked on New Year's Day." Apparently, in order to supernaturally cleanse themselves people would start by making a fire in "every room in the house and shutting up the house so that the smoke could not escape." Family members would suffer through the smoke for as long as they could before dashing into the fresh outside air. Once the entire family was in the clear, all of the pets and farm animals were treated to the same ritual. This bizarre custom was said "to be a charm to keep man and beast from harm during the coming year."

As you can see from the examples above, our modern celebrations can't hold a candle to the rituals of yesteryear—just make sure you don't let that candle leave your house on New Year's Day.

Chapter 15
La Befana: The Witch of Winter

After reading about numerous male creatures in this book, you may be wondering to yourself, where the heck are all of the female monsters? Well, don't worry, because strange winter beasts are equal opportunity terrorizers. You have Perchta-the pagan goddess of Christmas, Baba Yaga-the horribly deformed old woman of Russia, the Japanese vengeful winter spirit of Puki-onna, among countless other female entities ready to spoil your dark days and nights. However, it is the tragic story of La Befana, one that is so odd and filled with overwhelming guilt and regret, that places it among my favorite holiday legends.

Known throughout the world as the Witch of Italy, there are nearly as many different versions of the La Befana legend as there are people telling them. One commonly agreed upon hallmark of the legend involves the three wise men inviting Befana to join them on their quest to see the birth of Jesus. In their wonderful kids' book, *La Befana and The Star: The Christmas Gift From Italy,* Kate West and Ken Shuey tell of the wise men losing track of the brilliant bright star in the sky that had been guiding their route. Seeking some assistance, they stopped in at Befana's house to inquire about directions. As a gracious host, Befana invited them to dine and rest in the comfort of her sparklingly clean home (since she was a little child, Befana had been obsessed with cleaning and sweeping). After the delicious meal, the men noticed that the star was once again shining brightly in the night sky so they quickly set out to continue their travels. To repay Befana for her generosity and hospitality, the men invited Befana to join them in this once-in-a-lifetime journey. Obsessed with sweeping and cleanliness, Befana told them she had too much housework to do and declined the offer. As she was busily cleaning up the mess, Befana began to wonder if she had made a mistake in turning down such a wonderful opportunity. After a few hours of ruminating over her mistake, Befana quickly gathered her broom and a bag of gifts for the new king and set out in search of the wise men. She looked far and wide, but it was no use, the wise men were nowhere to be found. Overcome with guilt and regret, Befana made a vow that to serve as her penance, she would deliver a gift to each child until she found the right house, regardless of how long it took.

Somewhere along the way Befana was gifted with the magical power to fly about on her broom. Some say it was the spirit of the star that granted her this power, while others tell of her encountering a supernatural spirit. Regardless of how she obtained her magic, Befana could now cover vast distances in one night, and so it became that on Epiphany Eve (The evening of January 5 into January 6) Befana flies around bringing presents to well-behaved children.

Physically, La Befana has a striking appearance. Often, she is depicted as an old hag-like woman that is draped in a black shawl and scraggly garb. Her face and clothes are covered in soot, due to the fact that she enters homes through the chimney. In fact, the legend of La Befana shares many interesting similarities with Santa Claus. She, too, leaves out coal for those whose behavior has been less than stellar. Sometimes in her cruelty she leaves naughty children onions or garlic to rub in the lack of candy left behind. For those lucky children who made her nice list, Befana leaves behind an assortment of toys, candy, and fruit, often in stockings. If a child has shown truly exceptional behavior, Befana will even sweep up and clean their house. However, it should be noted that similar to how kids need to be sleeping in order for Santa to show up, it is advised against waiting up to encounter Befana, because if she catches you spying on her, she will attack you with her broom. If you happen to hear anything out of the ordinary on Epiphany Eve you best hustle to your bed and get some sleep.

Chapter 16
Lumberjacks and Their
Winter Creatures

Beginning in the mid-1800s thousands of men throughout the country left their families, farms, and hometowns in order to spend the winter up in the Northwoods cutting trees. Logging was done during the winter months for several key reasons. First, the cold weather cut down on all the bloodthirsty mosquitoes, wood ticks, and pesky insects that plagued the big woods. The ice and snow also provided the perfect conditions on the tote-roads for hauling timber. The slickness of the roads made it much easier for the horses and oxen to pull the heavy sleighs down to the river's edge. In the spring, the melting snow raised the rivers high enough that all the previously cut logs could be floated downriver to sawmills.

Winter also provided the most terrifying creatures that the lumberjacks could ever imagine. After an extremely long and exhausting day of cutting trees, the lumberjacks would retreat to their bunkhouse for a precious few hours before sleep overtook them. As the winds blew and the snow howled outside in the pitch-black darkness, the lumberjacks would sit in their bunks, smoke their pipes, and tell tall-tales to the greenhorns (young rookies). The big woods of the north seemed inexhaustible, a never-ending sprawl of dense forest where anything was not just possible, but probable. Here are a couple of the winter-only monsters that the lumberjacks had to deal with.

The Snow Snake

The snow snake is a snake that hibernates all spring, summer, and fall, and only comes out after the first winter snow. Except for its pale blue eyes (some say pink), its entire body is snowy white, which makes it nearly impossible to spot because it perfectly blends in with the fresh winter snow. The true origin of the snow snake is anyone's guess. In his 1939 book *Fearsome Critters*, Henry Tryon claimed that during the year of the two winters, "these pink-eyed, white bodied savage serpents crossed over from Siberia." Others contend that they are a native inhabitant of the Northwoods, but until fairly recently, their mastery of using the snow as camouflage had just kept them undiscovered.

Minnesota's first state forester, William T. Cox, told many newspapers that the snow snake survives almost entirely on snowshoe hares that it voraciously hunts. In the late 1920s and early 1930s, Art Childs wrote a series of weekly national newspaper articles under the heading of *"Yarns of the Big Woods."* In his article on the snow snake, Childs expanded on the creature's hunting preferences claiming, "They are supposed to live on owls, weasels, and other birds and animals." Being so adept at stealth, it seems probable that the snake could eat whatever animals it wanted.

In 1954, the *High Point Enterprise* ran a fascinating story detailing the clever means which Native Peoples had devised to capture the snake. Due to the snake's fondness for sweets, they would use black gumdrops to discover its location. Apparently, "The snow snake hunter places a few of these tidbits on the snow" and then watches closely. Eventually, the hungry snake will make a search for hard-to-find winter food and fall for the gum drop bait. As soon as a drop disappears, a hunter can grab at the exact spot where the drop was and snatch up the snow snake. Over time it was discovered that these snakes actually enjoyed black cough drops above all other treats. However, unlike in humans, the cough drops actually caused the snake to suffer a severe coughing fit that would cause it to turn blue and become visible against the snow.

Just like an ordinary snake, the snow snake can bite you, and since it is perfectly camouflaged by the bright white snow, you will probably never even see it coming. Its bite is fatal, but not because of any powerful venom. Instead, if you are bitten by a snow snake you will freeze to death.

Thankfully, science was able to find an antidote that could save the life of any unfortunate lumberjack that suffered the bite of a snow snake. In order to survive the bite, a lumberjack would have to consume a significant amount of booze. A 1958 article in the *Wisconsin State Journal* detailed just how much liquor it would take to cure a lumberjack, writing, "When he starts rocking around the stool and begins seeing things that aint there, he is in the clear." Luckily, snow snake bites were only thought to last a couple of hours so that "by that time a feller auta be fulla tonic."

The Furry Trout

In order to survive and flourish in the Northwoods, many species have to adjust to the extreme harshness of winter. Creatures either find ways to acclimate to the brutal winters or they perish. Perhaps the greatest transformation comes in the form of the Furry Trout. The Furry Trout is nearly identical to its southern trout cousins except for the amazing fact that it has grown a thick coat of fur to insulate it from the chilled waters of the north.

It is not known when these remarkable animals first began changing from an ordinary trout to that of the fur-bearing variety. A 1938 article in the *Hammond Times* claimed that "Tales of the furry fin-flippers have circulated here since Zebulon Pike first glimpsed the Rocky Mountains."

According to a 1936 article in the *Winona Republican,* Fred Kranhold, a Wisconsin fisherman, "had produced the furry trout of the Latin genus 'furre piscis,'" which had caught Minnesota anglers off guard, even though no photographic evidence was produced.

In 1938, the town of Salida, Colorado, announced its belief that the furry trout had once swum in their rivers. In an attempt to explain the marked decrease of Furry Trout sightings, the paper opined that perhaps the trout "were mistaken for beavers and exterminated by trappers," or "the flow of hot springs into the river has caused them to shed their fur. If there are any left, they're not as fur-bearing as they were."

The Snow Wasset

The Snow Wasset is the most proficient and voracious hunter the Northwoods has ever produced. On any given day it would eat a wide assortment of varmints, including grouse, rabbits, fox, raccoons, and the occasional lumberjack. Thought to have been stranded in the north when the glaciers retreated during the last ice age, the creature has seamlessly adapted to the harsh conditions of its environment.

The best physical description of the Snow Wasset came from the *Spokesman Review,* which claimed it had a "head and fur like a polar bear and a body like a sea lion." The *Kansas Star* said it looked "for all the world like a huge walrus."

One amazing trait of the Snow Wasset is the weird metamorphosis that it goes through each year. In the winter the beast is pure white, blending perfectly with the bright snow. Its legless body allows it to stealthily slide under the snow like a seal where it sneaks up on its oblivious prey. With the spring warming, the Snow Wasset sprouts rudimentary legs and is able to awkwardly amble about in the shade. Its fur takes on a dark forest green coloration that helps camouflage it from any hungry predators. The Wasset likes to estivate (hibernate) during the warmest months when its fur turns green and it finds wet moss or cranberry marshes to settle down in. In 1910, William Cox documented what happened after every first snowstorm of the season, writing, "The Wasset sheds its legs and starts south, dipping about in the snow. It soon attains remarkable skill in this method of travel." In 1924, the *Kansas Star* provided a fascinating overview of the Wasset's hunting ability, writing, "It hunts by lying under a snowbank, and when it hears something passing over its head it reaches out and pulls it down under the surface." Apparently, not even wolves and bears were safe from the Wasset. This hunting prowess was echoed by the *Montana Standard,* which wrote of the huge number of "poorly adapted animals and woodsmen" that fell victim to the Wasset.

Chapter 17
Babe the Blue Ox: Paul
Bunyan's Winter Discovery

While nearly everyone is familiar with Paul Bunyan's gigantic blue
best friend, not many are aware of how Paul and Babe actually met.
It happened during the winter of the blue snow—a winter that produced such severe freezing temperatures that people cursed a blue

streak so long it turned the snow from white to blue. It was during the blue winter when Paul was making his rounds through camp, he discovered a calf stuck in the snow, frozen stiff like a board. Babe, who began life as a normal white calf, had been out in the elements so long his skin had turned blue. Paul immediately took him inside to recover, and like everything around Paul Bunyan, Babe grew to an enormous size—and he kept his blue coloring.

Paul and Babe were responsible for creating much of America's landscape. Dragging his ax behind him as he walked, Paul dug out the Grand Canyon. Paul and Babe's massive footprints created Minnesota's 10,000 lakes, and the Dakotas are mostly devoid of trees because of the logging prowess of the twosome. While Paul and Babe were hauling their water container it sprang a leak, flowed south and created the Mississippi River.

You are probably wondering . . . just how big is Babe? The most accurate calculation of Babe's size came from those who worked with him as collected by folklorist Dorothy Moulding Brown who, in her book *What Say of You Paul,* described Babe as being "sixty hands high," and weighing "ten thousand pounds." Babe measured "seven axe-handles and a plug of Star tobacco between the eyes," and the tips of his long horns were "forty-two peavy handles apart." Such was the size of Babe that lumberjacks tied a string up between his horns and made such a long clothesline that all the camp's clothes could be hung out at the same time. The mind-blowing number of amazing tales surrounding Babe the Blue Ox rivals those of Paul himself. Author Brian Gleeson captured several of these yarns in his book, *Paul Bunyan*. For example, if you watched Babe for five minutes you would see him grow right in front of you. Babe pulled a loaded sled so hard "he would straighten the chain that held it into a solid bar." Many of the old tote roads were a nasty series of winding twists, turns, and dangerous curves. If you saw these roads from the sky, you would think they spelled out every letter in the alphabet. Of course, these tangled roads only made hauling lumber more difficult so Paul came up with a brilliant idea—he hooked Babe up to one end of the road and told him to pull as hard as he could. Babe was so powerful he pulled out all the kinks and made the road straight as an arrow. The endless miles of extra roads were used to make America's first roads.

Chapter 18
Predicting Winter Weather

For most of America's modern history, the overwhelming majority of people lived and worked on farms. This self-sustaining lifestyle often teetered on disaster, which presented the real possibility that if your crops failed or your livestock went ill, you might not survive the season. One of the most critical components predicting your success on the farm was one in which you could not control—the weather! Generations of accumulated knowledge rewarded those who had a keen eye to help thwart the fickle nature of Mother Nature. Having the skills to accurately predict impending weather could shift the balance of your farm's achievement from catastrophe to triumph. The ever-increasing shift of Americans leaving the farm and rural communities in order to live in larger towns and cities has dramatically wiped away this important folk knowledge of winter. Luckily, some stewards of this material, like the *Farmers' Almanac*, which has been publishing yearly weather predictions since 1792, continue to harvest these important weather predictions tools and signs. So, if you ever want to know more than checking out your neighbor's hilarious sign that reads—if this sign is wet, it is raining—I have included some of the most interesting predictors of a hard winter below.

Most of the weather prognosticating involves looking for signs that portend a hard winter. For instance, it is believed that if you notice that caterpillars have extra bushy bristles, it means that a harsh winter is on its way. In the same manner, if the squirrel in your backyard also displays an extra bushy tail, you are in store for a terrible winter. If you start to see your horses and cows are displaying thicker coats and hair, you best get out your warm winter coat. I have to be honest in saying that many of us in today's world would have an extremely hard time determining whether or not the squirrel in our back yard has an extra bushy tail. The same goes for the rest of the above-mentioned signs, however, there is one sign that even the most oblivious of observers among us can pick up on—and that is if you see two woodpeckers in the same tree, it means old man winter is angry.

Winter is not the only season to enjoy nature's predictive signs, in the 2023 *Farmer's Almanac*, they cover several other plant folklore that can alert you to odd weather, including the idea that those annoying dandelions from your front yard can feel rain coming. Apparently, "these herb-flowers close when they detect moisture and reopen when the weather dries." Even more amazing is the Scarlet Pimpernel—routinely called a poor man's weather glass, which can predict rain as its "blooms remain open in full sun, but when the skies turn cloudy or humidity reaches 80%, they fold up like little rain shy umbrellas." Even pine cones react to humidity. If the air is dry expect to see their scales jut out like a Christmas tree. However, if the air reaches high humidity, the scales will clam up in anticipation of rain or snow.

Of course, these are just but a few of the countless weather predictors that exist in old wives' tales, superstitions, customs, and folklore. For those of you who are passionate about this subject, you will easily find a never-ending supply of these odd weather predictors, and for those of you in cold climates, it is always a good idea to simply hope for the best and plan for the worst.

Chapter 19
How to Bring About a Snow Day

As a kid, one of the benefits of living in a snow-filled climate is the possibility that one of those snowstorms will provide you with a glorious day off from school. On school nights, nothing was better than hearing the local meteorologist warning of an impending blizzard, as it meant that the following morning would most likely be school-free. Unfortunately, many of us were completely unaware that there are plenty of rituals you can follow to help give that snowstorm a nice little helpful push. Here are a few of my favorites:

1. Before heading to bed for the evening you can place a spoon under your pillow. Perhaps conflated with Tooth Fairy legends, or the old wives' tale of placing a knife under the bed of a woman in labor to help cut the pain, this custom is said to drastically increase the amount of snowfall that you will receive. A spoon left in the freezer is also said to have the same effect. Cotton balls (symbolizing snowballs) under the pillow will also do the trick.

2. In a similar vein to baseball players turning their hats inside out to help promote a rally, kids can turn their pajamas inside out and wear them backwards to increase the chances of a major snowfall visiting their area. Some say this bizarre clothing switch can also transform your luck from bad to good.

3. Some customs are just downright weird. To prove this point, I present the ice cube in the toilet method of creating snow. Some believe that merely throwing ice cubes into the toilet will equate to heavy snowfall. Others contend that it will snow one inch for every ice cube you toss into the toilet. Finally, the act of throwing ice cubes out the front door also will alert the Snow Gods to your plight.

4. Crayons are an important part of any childhood so it only seems fitting that the crayon would also play an important

role in producing a snow day. One legend tells that if you place a white crayon in the freezer and leave it there overnight or then place it under your pillow before bed, a heavy snowfall will follow. Another variation of this belief states that placing a crayon on the window sill is a surefire way to bring about snow. The color of the crayon varies as no definite color has been proven to outperform others, but the most popular colors are white and blue as they best represent cold and ice.

The next time you are in desperate need of a snow day from school (or work) feel free to try any of these measures, or better yet, try them all!

Chapter 20
The Battle to be the
Ice-Box of the Nation

Believe it or not, there are several cities throughout America that are actively fighting for the right to be called the "Ice-Box of the Nation." Looking to celebrate their physical and mental hardiness, or perhaps tout their wonderful winter activities, these cities see the Ice-Box moniker as a way to lure in winter tourism and to boost communal pride.

Since the 1940s, the battle over which American town can lay official claim to the Ice-Box of the Nation slogan has been heating up!
Today, the town of International Falls, Minnesota, has been granted
the official title, but the other towns throw up their frozen hands
and scoff at the official title, firmly believing that, official or not, no
other town can come close to their winter hardship.

In order to try and settle this long-standing feud, let's take a look at
some of the top-ranked contenders:

1. International Falls, Minnesota—This perennial favor-
    ite sitting at the northern tip of Minnesota boasts of fre-
    quent minus 40-degree temperatures (without wind chill).
    Amazingly, the town simply shrugs off the freezing cold
    and celebrates its annual Ice-Box Days Winter festival—
    where every January visitors and townsfolk can partici-
    pate in the Freeze Yer Gizzard Blizzard Run, A snowman
    & snow sculpture contest, a scavenger hunt, and evening
    snowshoe hikes along with many other outdoor activities.

2. Big Piney, Wyoming—In a wonderful story on *National
    Public Radio's All Things Considered* show, one long-time
    resident of Big Piney stated that "if you spend a winter in
    her hometown almost 7,000 feet above sea level, you won't
    forget it." She continued, "All you have to do to a lot of
    people is mention Big Piney, and they said the worst winter

or few months I ever spent in my life was in Big Piney, Wyoming. It was so cold."

3. Fraser, Colorado—Fraser battled with International Falls for years in a tooth and nail legal struggle over the Ice-Box title. Eventually, with the help of a nice payment from International Falls, the town took to calling itself the Ice-Box of Colorado or Ice-Box of the Rockies. One thing is certain, winters in Fraser are long and cold.

4. Pellston, Michigan—In 1933, the temperature in Pellston dipped to a soul crushing -53 degrees (without wind chill). Every winter since the town has experienced such awfully frigid cold that it gives Floridians nightmares.

Today, the bragging rights battle over the Ice-Box of the Nation is far from over; the citizens of each city are firmly entrenched in their belief that they inhabit the harshest place in America. You might think this is a trivial matter, but the stakes are high, as great pride and a sense of honor come with such self-appointed accolades. Personally, as a native of northern Wisconsin, I can relate to all of the cities on this list, and at some point, when the temperatures dip below -20 degrees, cold is simply cold. In my book, all of these places deserve the right to call themselves whatever helps them battle their way through the unforgiving reality of living in such cold places. My only hope is that the great people of Alaska do not get wind of this title and decide to show all of us lower 48ers what true cold really looks like.

About the Author

Chad Lewis is an author, researcher, and lecturer on topics of the strange and unusual. The more bizarre the legend is, the more likely you will find him there.

About the Illustrator

Morgan Knudsen has been involved in the world of paranormal phenomena for 20 years. She is the author of two books—Teaching the Living: From Heartbreak to Happiness in a Haunted Home, and The Gift of Instinct: Paranormal Lessons for an Extraordinary World.